© 1997 Owl Wholesale Ltd
Published by Owl Wholesale Ltd
1 Stanaway Drive, Crumlin, Dublin 12, Ireland

First published 1997
Reprinted 2005, 2009

ISBN 978-1-85534-790-8

Printed and bound in Poland.

IRISH LEGENDS

St Patrick

Retold by Reg Keating
Illustrated by Martin Cater

Tarantula Books

Patrick was a happy young boy.
He lived in a land across the sea.

One day, Patrick heard voices on the wind.

The voices were coming across the sea from Ireland.

The voices were calling for someone to come and show the people of Ireland a better way of life.

At that time, the people of Ireland were all pagans.

They had strange gods. They had strange customs.

They were a war-like people who were always fighting.

They could not read or write.

While Patrick was listening to the voices, a long boat landed at the seashore.

Cruel and savage men jumped from the boat. They were raiders from Ireland.

They captured Patrick and tied him up.

They put him into the boat and brought him to Ireland.

Patrick was sold as a slave.
The man who bought Patrick was
called Milchu.

Milchu forced Patrick to work for him.

Patrick's work was minding sheep and
pigs high up on Mount Slemish in County
Antrim.

Patrick was cold and hungry. Worst of all, he was afraid of the snakes that crawled all over Mount Slemish.

Patrick spent seven long years minding pigs and sheep on Mount Slemish.

Every night and every day, he prayed for God to help him escape.

One night, Patrick heard a voice in a dream. The voice told him to go to the seashore.

Patrick went to the seashore and saw a boat getting ready to sail.

He climbed on board the boat and hid under a sack.

S oon the boat sailed out to sea. It landed near Patrick's home.

His mother and father were delighted to see Patrick safely home again.

Patrick had promised God that if he escaped from Ireland he would become a bishop.

P atrick kept his promise.

When Patrick was a bishop, he again heard voices in a dream.

They were the same voices that Patrick had first heard as a young boy.

This time the voices said, "Come back, Patrick, and walk once more among us."

The people of Ireland were asking Patrick to show them a better way of life.

Patrick knew that God wanted him to go back to Ireland.

This time he was not afraid.

He banished all the snakes from Ireland and drove them into the sea.

He banished the strange gods and customs of the people.

He picked up a shamrock to show them how three Gods could be in one.

The people of Ireland became Christians.

Every year on the seventeenth of March, people all over the world celebrate Saint Patrick's Day.